Nuffield Primary Science
SCIENCE PROCESSES AND CONCEPT EXPLORATION

Ages
5-7

Electricity and magnetism

TEACHERS' GUIDE

PUBLISHED FOR THE NUFFIELD–CHELSEA CURRICULUM TRUST BY COLLINS EDUCATIONAL

Trial schools

The SPACE Project and the Trust are grateful to the governors, staff, and pupils of all the trial schools. It will be obvious to readers of these publications how much we are indebted to them for their help, and especially for the children's drawn and written records of their hard work and their growing understanding of science.

All Saints Primary School, Barnet, Hertfordshire
Arnot County Primary Infant School, Arnot Street, Walton, Liverpool
Balladen Primary School, Rawtenstall, Rossendale
Blacko County Primary School, Blacko, Lancashire
Chalgrove JMI School, Finchley, London N3
Fairway JMI School, Mill Hill, London NW7
Fazakerley Junior School, Formosa Drive, Liverpool
Foulds Primary School, Barnet, Hertfordshire
Frenchwood County Primary School, Preston, Lancashire
Hillbrook Primary School, Tooting, London SW17
Mawdesley Church of England Primary School, Lancashire
Padiham Green Church of England Primary School, Padiham, Lancashire
Roe Lee County Primary School, Blackburn, Lancashire
St Aloysius Roman Catholic Infants School, Knowsley
St Ambrose Junior School, Alderfield Drive, Speke, Liverpool
St Hughes RC JMI School, Earle Road, Liverpool
St Michael in the Hamlet Infant School, Neilson Road, Liverpool
St Stephen's Church of England School, Burnley
St Theresa's Roman Catholic Primary School, Finchley, London N3
Salterforth Primary School, Salterforth, Lancashire
Snaresbrook Primary School, Wanstead, London E18
Stubbins Primary School, Ramsbottom, Lancashire
Thorn County Primary School, Cowtoot Lane, Bacup, Lancashire
Trawden County Primary School, Dean Street, Trawden, Lancashire
Walton-le-Dale County Primary School, Preston
Water County Primary School, Burnley Road East, Water, Rossendale
Waterfoot County Primary School, Thornfield Avenue, Waterfoot, Rossendale
Whittlefield Infant School, Tabor Street, Burnley, Lancashire
Woodridge Primary School, North Finchley, London N12

Contents

Explanation of symbols in the margins

 Warning

 Good opportunities to develop and assess work related to Experimental and Investigative Science.

 Notes which may be useful to the teacher

 Vocabulary work

 Opportunities for children to use information technology

 Equipment needed

 Reference to the pupils' books

CHAPTER 1

Planning

1.1 The SPACE approach to teaching and learning science

A primary class where the SPACE approach to science is being used may not at first seem different from any other class engaged in science activities; in either, children will be mentally and physically involved in exploring objects and events in the world around them. However, a closer look will reveal that both the children's activities and the teacher's role differ from those found in other approaches. The children are not following instructions given by others; they are not solving a problem set them by someone else. They are deeply involved in work which is based on their own ideas, and they have taken part in deciding how to do it.

The teacher has, of course, prepared carefully to reach the point where children try out their ideas. She or he will have started on the topic by giving children opportunities to explore from their own experience situations which embody important scientific ideas. The teacher will have ensured that the children have expressed their ideas about what they are exploring, using one or more of a range of approaches – from whole class discussion to talking with individual children, or asking children to write or draw – and will have explored the children's reasons for having those ideas.

With this information the teacher will have decided how to help the children to develop or revise their ideas. That may involve getting the children to use the ideas to make a prediction, then testing it by seeing if it works in practice; or the children may gather further evidence to discuss and think about. In particular, the teacher will note how 'scientific' children have been in their gathering and use of evidence; and should, by careful questioning, encourage greater rigour in the use of scientific process skills.

It is essential that it is the children who change their ideas as a result of what they find themselves, and that they are not merely accepting ideas which they are told are better.

By carefully exploring children's ideas, taking them seriously and choosing appropriate ways of helping the children to test them, the teacher can move children towards ideas which apply more widely and fit the evidence better – those which are, in short, more scientific.

You will find more information about the SPACE approach in the Nuffield Primary Science *Science Co-ordinators' handbook*.

1.2 Useful strategies

Finding out children's ideas

This guide points out many opportunities for finding out children's ideas. One way is simply by talking, but there are many others. We have found the following strategies effective. How you use them may depend on the area of science you are dealing with. In the teachers' guides you will find examples of these strategies, with suggestions as to where you might use them. More information about them is given in the *Science Co-ordinators' handbook.*

Talking and open questioning

Whole class discussions can be useful for sharing ideas, but they do not always give all children a chance to speak. It is often helpful if children are allowed to think of their own ideas first, perhaps working them out in drawings, and are then encouraged to share these with others – perhaps with just one other child, or with a larger group.

Annotated drawings

Asking children to draw their ideas can give a particularly clear insight into what they think. It also gives you a chance to discuss the children's ideas with them. Words conveying these ideas can then be added to the drawing, either by you or by the child, in the course of discussion to clarify what has been represented. Such work can be kept as a permanent record.

Sorting and classifying

This can be a useful way of helping children to clarify their ideas and to record their thinking. They could sort a collection of objects or pictures into groups.

Writing down ideas

When they have acquired some writing skill, this gives children the opportunity to express their own views. It will usually be in response to questions posed by you.

Log books and diaries

These can be used to record changes over a longer period of time. They need not necessarily be kept by individual children, but could be kept by a group or class as a whole. Children can jot down, as words or drawings, the changes they notice and something about what they think are the reasons for what they observe.

Helping children to develop their ideas

Letting children try out their own ideas

This will involve children in using some of the process skills of science: at first mainly observing, predicting, and communicating. Later, as children approach Key Stage 2, they will begin to make more use of measuring, hypothesizing, planning and carrying out fair tests, and interpreting results and findings.

As often as possible, children should see what happens when they put their ideas to test. They should be encouraged to observe and report carefully what happens and to give their ideas about why it happens.

Encouraging generalization from one context to another

In discussing a particular event, for example dissolving sugar in tea, consider whether the explanation proposed applies in another context, such as salt dissolving on a wet road. You or the children might suggest other contexts where the idea might be tried. This might be done by discussing the evidence for and against the explanation, or by gathering more evidence and testing the idea in the other context, depending on children's familiarity with the events being examined.

Discussing the words children use to describe their ideas

Children can be asked to be quite specific about the meaning of words they use, whether scientific or not. They can be prompted to think of alternative words which have almost the same meaning. They can be asked to think of examples of a word they are using, such as 'melt', so that you can decide when to introduce alternative or more precise words if necessary.

Extending the range of evidence

Some of the children's ideas may be consistent with their experience up to that time, but they could be challenged by extending the range of this experience. This applies particularly to things which are not easily observed, such as slow changes; or those which are normally hidden, such as the insides of objects. Books are useful in some cases.

Getting children to communicate their ideas

Expressing ideas in any way – through writing, drawing, modelling or, particularly, through discussion – involves thinking them through, and often rethinking and revising them. Discussion has a further advantage in that it is two-way and children can set others' ideas against their own. Just realizing that there are different ideas helps them to reconsider their own.

1.3 Charts to help children to develop their ideas

The charts on pages 20, 27 and 35 show how you can help children to develop their ideas from starting points which have given rise to different ideas.

The centre rectangles contain starter questions.
The surrounding 'thought bubbles' contain the sort of ideas expressed by children.
The further ring of rectangles contains questions posed by teachers in response to the ideas expressed by the children. These questions are meant to prompt children to think about their ideas.
The outer rounded boxes indicate ways in which the children might respond to the teacher's questions.
Some of the shapes have been left blank, as a sign that other ideas may be encountered and other ways of helping children to develop their ideas may be tried.

This teachers' guide is divided into themes; in each one there is a section on finding out children's ideas, examples of ideas children have, and a section on helping children to develop their ideas.

1.4 Electricity and magnetism and the curriculum

Sources and uses of electricity

This theme aims to help children develop their ideas about how electricity is supplied and used, sources of electricity, and dangers associated with electricity.

Children suggest a variety of sources from which we get electricity, for example, lightning water and the Sun. Some children think that electricity comes from electrical appliances such as the telephone and the TV. Many children are aware that electricity makes some domestic appliances work, and that electricity is 'dangerous'.

There are suggestions for helping children to become more aware of the range of electrical appliances in the home and school, how electricity reaches electrical appliances, electrical safety and the use of batteries.

Children are encouraged to use electricity safely, to understand that batteries give a safe form of electricity, and are introduced to ideas about connecting batteries in circuits and electrical devices. Some of the ideas developed here are needed for activities in the circuits theme.

National Curriculum Programme of Study

Physical Processes

1 Electricity
a that many everyday appliances use electricity.

Environmental Studies 5-14 (Scotland): Science

Understanding Energy and Forces (Stages P1 to P3)

Properties and uses of energy
• everyday uses of these forms of energy in common devices, eg cooker, candle, bell;
• safe use of energy providers.

Making circuits

The aim of this theme is to introduce children to the idea of a complete electrical circuit which is needed for constructing more complex circuits at KS2.

Many children are unaware that batteries and electrical components have two connection points, and often try to connect a single wire to an electrical component and a battery. Although children may be able to construct a complete circuit for a bulb, they may be uncertain of how other components could be connected into a circuit.

Within this theme there are suggestions for helping children to construct simple circuits for a bulb, or a buzzer, together with ways of helping them to devise their own switches and test the electrical conduction of materials. The ideas developed here will help children to construct simple circuits in models and electrical games.

Magnets

This theme helps children to develop their ideas about properties of magnets, and apply their ideas in designing magnetic games and appliances.

Many children know that magnets attract objects, but they may be uncertain of the type of material that is attracted, and unaware of magnetic repulsion between magnets. Some young children regard magnets as 'magical', while others may describe them as full of 'energy' or 'glue'.

There are suggestions for using magnets in games and household appliances, and investigations in which children can find out about their properties.

The experiences in this theme prepare children for investigations at KS2 in which they begin to find out about the magnetic effects of an electric current.

Physical Processes

1 Electricity
b to construct simple circuits involving batteries, wires, bulbs and buzzers;
c that electrical devices will not work if there is a break in the circuit.

Physical Processes

2 Forces and motion
b that both pushes and pulls are examples of forces.

Materials and their Properties

1 Grouping materials
b to sort materials into groups on the basis of simple properties, including texture, appearance, transparency and whether they are magnetic or non-magnetic.

1.5 Experimental and Investigative Science

Two important aspects of children's learning in science are:

◆ learning how to investigate the world around them;
◆ learning to make sense of the world around them using scientific ideas.

These are reflected in the National Curriculum. 'Experimental and Investigative Science' covers the first aspect. The second aspect is covered by the rest of the Programme of Study. Although these two aspects of science learning are separated in the National Curriculum they cannot be separated in practice and it is not useful to try to do so. Through investigation children explore their ideas and/or test out the ideas which arise from discussion. As a result, ideas may be advanced, but this will depend on the children's investigation skills. Thus it is important to develop these skills in the context of activities which extend ideas. So there is no separate Nuffield Primary Science teachers' guide on scientific investigations, because opportunities to make these occur throughout all the guides and they form an essential part of the SPACE approach.

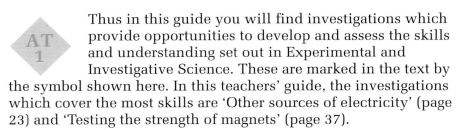

Thus in this guide you will find investigations which provide opportunities to develop and assess the skills and understanding set out in Experimental and Investigative Science. These are marked in the text by the symbol shown here. In this teachers' guide, the investigations which cover the most skills are 'Other sources of electricity' (page 23) and 'Testing the strength of magnets' (page 37).

It is important that teachers give active guidance to pupils during investigations to help them work out how to improve the way in which they plan and carry out their investigations.

Experimental and Investigative Science is about the ways scientific evidence can be obtained, about the ways observations and measurements are made, and about the way in which the evidence is analysed. It therefore sets out three main ways in which pupils can develop their ability to do experimental and investigative science, as follows:-

1 'Planning experimental work'. Here, children should be helped to make progress from asking general and vague questions, to suggesting ideas which could be tested. Teachers' discussion with pupils should aim to help them to make predictions, using their existing understanding, on the basis of which they can decide what evidence should be collected. This should lead them to think about what apparatus and equipment they should use.

When children describe plans for their work, they should be helped to think about what features they are going to change, what effects of these changes they are going to observe or measure, and what features they must keep the same. In this way they can come to understand what is meant by 'a fair test'.

2 'Obtaining evidence'. Children should make observations in the light of their ideas about what they are looking for and why. When they describe their observations, teachers may have to help them to improve, for example by reminding them of their original aims and plan for the work. Such help should also encourage progress from qualitative comparisons and judgements to appreciating the value of making quantitative measurements (for example 'cold water' is qualitative, 'water at 12°C' is quantitative). This should lead to the development of skills with a variety of instruments and to increasing care and accuracy in measurement, involving, for example, repeating measurements to check.

3 'Considering evidence'. Here, children should first learn to record their evidence in systematic and clear ways, starting with simple drawings and then learning to use tables, bar charts and line graphs to display the patterns in numerical data. Then they should be asked to think about and discuss their results, considering what might be learnt from any trends or patterns. As ideas develop, they should be careful in checking their evidence against the original idea underlying the investigation and should become increasingly critical in discussing alternative explanations which might fit their evidence. In such discussions, they should be helped to relate their arguments to their developing scientific understanding. They should also be guided to see possibilities for conducting their investigation more carefully, or in quite different ways.

Whilst these three may seem to form a natural sequence of stages, children's work might not follow this particular sequence. For example, some might start with evidence from their observations and proceed on this basis to propose a hypothesis and a plan to test it. For others, the results of one task may be the starting point for a new inquiry involving new measurements. Useful learning about how to investigate might arise when only one or two of the above aspects of an investigation are involved, or when the teacher tells children about some aspects so that they can concentrate on others. However, there should be some occasions for all pupils when they carry out the whole process of investigation by themselves.

The assessment examples given in chapter 3 are analysed in relation to the level descriptions, which describe children's progress in relation to these three aspects: *planning experimental work*, *obtaining evidence* and *considering evidence*. Thus, these three provide a framework both for guiding children and for assessing their progress in experimental and investigative work.

1.6 Planning your science programme in school

The following pages give examples of how two schools have planned their science programme for the whole of Key Stage 1. Planning of this kind helps to provide continuity and progression in children's learning in science. The development of such whole school programmes is discussed more fully in the *Science Co-ordinators' Handbook*.

Each plan covers the requirements for the National Curriculum at Key Stage 1 and shows which themes in the Nuffield Primary Science Teachers' Guides have been used for planning the topic in detail by the classteacher.

Example 1

This primary school has recently grown from 1.5 form entry to 2 form entry and so have had to take account of varying class sizes and vertical grouping. Their programme is based on fixed year topics which provide progression through the programme of study but by using the SPACE approach staff feel they are able to cater for individual children.

Each topic is planned out, by year group, in terms of the concept to be explored and the key ideas to be focused on using the Teachers' Guides. Some topics run for one term whilst others are restricted to half a term. A minimum of five lessons are allowed for each half term. Individual teachers use the topic plan to develop their own short term planning responding to the ideas of the children in their class.

	AUTUMN TERM	SPRING TERM		SUMMER TERM	
RECEPTION	Individual variation	Sources and uses of electricity	Light and dark	Changing materials	
Nuffield Primary Science Teachers' Guide	The variety of life 2.2	Electricity and magnetism 2.1	Light 2.1, 2.2	Materials 2.2	
Programme of Study †	Sc2:4a	Sc4:1a	Sc4:3a, b	Sc3:2a, b; Sc4:2d	
YEAR 1	Pushes and pulls	Making and hearing sounds	The human body and keeping healthy	Local habitats	Plants and animal growth
Nuffield Primary Science Teachers' Guide	Forces and movement 2.1 Using energy 2.2	Sound and music 2	Living processes 2.2	Living things in their environment 2.1 Rocks, soil and weather 2.1 Earth in space 2.3	Living processes 2.3
Programme of Study †	Sc4:2a, b, c, d	Sc4:3c, d, e	Sc2:2a, b, c, d, e, f	Sc2:5a, b	Sc2:2e; 3a, b, c
YEAR 2	Properties of materials	Magnets	Electricity - simple circuits	Naming and grouping living things	
Nuffield Primary Science Teachers' Guide	Materials 2.1 Rocks, soil and weather 2.1	Electricity and magnetism 2.3	Electricity and magnetism 2.2	The variety of life 2.1	
Programme of Study †	Sc3:1a, b, c, d, e	Sc3:1b, c	Sc4:1a, b, c	Sc2:1a, b; 4b	

8

Example 2

Situated in a large conurbation this primary school is 2.5 form entry but the number of children entering fluctuates from year to year causing difficulties with class size. The Nursery is an integral part of the school and work is shared with the Reception classes. Therefore this pre-YR1 time is planned as a whole providing a wide range of experiences for the children so that they are 'working towards' the requirements of the programme of study.

The plan is set out by year group and the different elements of the Programme of Study, covering five topics per year with each one to be covered in approximately half a term. Each year group decides the order of their topics during the year. The provision of a 'spare' half term allows teachers some flexibility in their planning and, if they wish, to introduce other aspects of science not prescribed by the National Curriculum.

	AUTUMN TERM		SPRING TERM		SUMMER TERM	
RECEPTION	This is me	Our school	Plants and animals	Homes - using electricity	Toys	
Nuffield Primary Science Teachers' Guide	The variety of life 2.2	Living things in their environment 2.3	Living things in their environment 2.1; Living processes 2.3	Electricity and magnetism 2.1	Forces and movement 2.1	
Programme of Study (working toward) †	Sc2:2a, b, f; 4a	Sc2:1a, 3b, 5a; Sc3:2a	Sc2:1b, 3a, b, c, 4b, 5a, b	Sc4:1a, 3a, b	Sc4:2a, b, c	
YEAR 1	Ourselves	Growing things	Materials - clothes	Sounds/Night and day	Floating and sinking	
Nuffield Primary Science Teachers' Guide	Living processes 2.2; Variety of life 2.2	Living processes 2.3	Materials 2.1	Sound and music 2; The earth in space 2.1	Forces and movement 2.2	
Programme of Study †	Sc2:1b; 2a, b, e, f; 4a, b	Sc2:3a, b, c	Sc3:1a, b, c, d, e; 2a	Sc4:3c, d, e	Sc3:1a, c, e; Sc4:2a	
YEAR 2	Keeping healthy	Habitats	Materials - homes	Light and electricity	Moving things	
Nuffield Primary Science Teachers' Guide	Living processes 2.2	The variety of life 2.1; Living things in their environment 2.1; Rocks, soil and weather 2.1	Materials 2.1; 2.2	Electricity and magnetism 2.1, 2.2; Light 2.1; 2.2	Forces and movement 2.1; Using energy 2.2	
Programme of Study †	Sc2:1b; 2b, c, d	Sc2:4b; 5a, b	Sc3:1a, b, c, d, e; 2b	Sc4:1a, b, c; 3a, b	Sc4:2a, b, c, d	

† For the purposes of these charts the references to sections of the Programme of Study have been abbreviated as follows:

Sc2 = Life Processes and Living Things
Sc3 = Materials and their Properties
Sc4 = Physical Processes

1.7 Planning a topic

Here is a case study which may help you in planning a topic.

Case study: Homes

The teacher had decided to place the study of electricity within the topic of homes. Children could use their experiences at home when looking at the sources and uses of electricity. The teacher also recognized the potential within the topic to make links with other curriculum areas. She planned that all children would be working on the same curriculum area at the same time, although they were often working on different issues within that aspect of the curriculum. Heavy demands on equipment for electrical circuits meant that within the lesson some of the class investigated circuits while others found out about the sources and uses of electricity.

Sources and uses of electricity

◆ Children drew the items in their homes which used electricity. They described to each other how the items were used and guessed the appliance described.

◆ Children discussed how they might be harmed by the electrical items and how they should be used carefully. They produced posters showing other children their ideas.

◆ Through discussion and secondary sources children explored their ideas of how electricity gets to their homes.

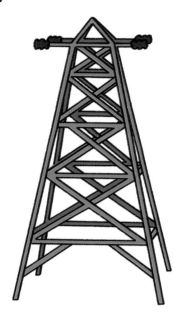

Making circuits

◆ Following an exploration of circuits children began to make lights for a house and a street.

Living things in their environment

The children made a list of all the animals they had seen in the school garden.

bee
bird
snail
caterpillar
worm

◆ They visited the garden at different times on different days and recorded which animals were there.

- ◆ They noticed whether the garden was light or damp and discussed why it would be a good place for some animals to live.
- ◆ Using pictures, they found other animals that live in different places and exchanged ideas about why these animals might live in a particular place.

LINKS WITH OTHER CURRICULUM AREAS

Mathematics

- ◆ Children made graphs of the different types of houses around the school.
- ◆ They looked at the shapes of windows, doors, brick and tile patterns.
- ◆ They measured the size of different rooms using body measurements such as strides.

Geography

- ◆ Children surveyed the variety of buildings in their surroundings and the way these buildings were used.
- ◆ They made simple maps of the locality based on their observations.
- ◆ Using pictures, children considered the variety of places where people live, and how the style of home can be related to the climate and landscape of different countries.

History

- ◆ Children looked at houses near school and tried to determine which were old and which were new.
- ◆ They discussed the evidence they had used to make their decisions.
- ◆ Some of the houses were Victorian, and children compared Victorian homes with modern homes.
- ◆ Children made a time line showing how houses had changed.

1.8 Pupils' books

The pupils' book accompanying this guide is called *A First look at electricity and magnets*. The pupils' books are intended to be used spread by spread. The spreads are not sequential, and they are covered in these notes in thematic order.

Features of the pupils' books include:
◆ Stimulus spreads, often visual, designed to raise questions, arouse curiosity, and to promote discussion.

◆ Information spreads, which give secondary source material in a clear and attractive way.

◆ Activity ideas, to form the basis of investigations to be carried out by the children.

◆ Cross-curricular spreads and stories which can act as a basis for creative writing, or spreads with a historical or creative focus.

◆ Real life examples of applications of science in the everyday world.

Keeping safe pages 2–3

Purpose: To provide warnings about electrical safety.
Note: Children could discuss what is happening in each of the pictures, saying why they think it is dangerous.
Teachers' guide cross-reference: *Electricity and magnetism*, page 21.

The mouse who knew better pages 4–5

Purpose: A story board for children to explain.
Note: The mouse spots the potential dangers in each picture.
Teachers' guide cross-reference: *Electricity and magnetism*, pages 21-2.

Electricity in the street pages 20–21

Purpose: To look at familiar uses of electricity.
Note: Children could discuss the different uses of electricity in the street.
Teachers' guide cross-reference: Electricity and magnetism, page 22.

Docklands light railway pages 14–15

Purpose: To introduce the idea of an electrically powered transport system.
Teachers' guide cross-reference: Electricity and magnetism, pages 21-2.

Electricity in the home pages 12–13

Purpose: A starting point for a discussion about saving energy.
Questions for discussion: What have they been told at home about using electricity around the house, and about saving energy? Discuss the uses of energy in the home.

Extension activity: Ask the children to draw a room showing things which use electricity. They could make a model of a room from a cardboard box, decorate it and add a light and switch.
Teachers' guide cross-reference: *Electricity and magnetism*, page 22.

Things which use batteries pages 8–9

Purpose: A discussion activity.
Notes: The following use batteries: the keyboard; the spelling game; the watch; the bulldozer; the aircraft game; the karaoke machine; the walking doll; the torch; the sewing machine; the white dog.
Extension activity: Children could draw some of their own toys which use batteries.
Teachers' guide cross-reference: *Electricity and magnetism*, page 23.

Milk float pages 10–11

Purpose: To show an example of a larger object that needs batteries.
Note: This spread introduces the idea that the milk float's battery has to be recharged.
Extension activities: Suggest the children work on the theme of transport. The children could write their own 'Story of the milk float'.
Teachers' guide cross-reference: *Electricity and magnetism*, page 23.

One hundred years ago pages 22–23

Purpose: To introduce children to the idea of a world without electricity.
Notes: In the matching exercise: the computer word processor matches the drawing of a typewriter; the modern vacuum cleaner matches with the vacuum cleaner with a bellows; the personal stereo matches with the cylinder that plays waxed cylinders; and the electric light matches with the candlelight.
Teachers' guide cross-reference: Electricity and magnetism, page 11.

Where does electricity come from? pages 16–17

Purpose: Information about the sources and distribution of electricity.
Notes: Use the pupils' book as a secondary source of information after the class have shared their own ideas about where electricity comes from. The class could draw where they think electricity comes from.
Teachers' guide cross-references: Electricity and magnetism, pages 27-8.

Switch it on! pages 18–19

Purpose: Information about different types of switches.
Teachers' guide cross-reference: *Electricity and magnetism*, page 29.

Magnets pages 6–7

Purpose: A starting point for a discussion of some common uses of magnets.
Question for discussion: Where have you seen magnets in daily life?
Teachers' guide cross-references: *Electricity and magnetism*, pages 32–40; *Forces and movement*, pages 10-11.

1.9 Resources

This is what you may need to carry out the investigations shown in this book.

Batteries: a selection (see 'Warnings' below)
Collection of solar powered items, such as toys, games, watches, calculators
Connecting wires, crocodile clips, bulb holders, buzzers, motors, switches, bulbs
Materials for making switches: drawing pins, small softwood blocks, paper clips, Plasticine, aluminium foil
Collection of torches
Transparent, translucent and opaque materials
Collection of common materials and objects which can be tested for electrical conductivity, magnetic properties
Collection of magnets: bar magnets, horseshoe magnets, ring magnets, magnetic door stickers; there should be a variety of size of magnet and of magnetic strength
Magnetic games

1.10 Warnings

Activities which need particular care are indicated by this symbol in the margin. Everything possible should be done to ensure the safety of the children during their investigations. You should consult any guidelines produced by your school or Local Education Authority and, if your school or LEA is a member, by CLEAPSS. LEAs often have special rules for Early Years. See also the Association for Science Education publication *Be safe! some aspects of safety in school science and technology for Key Stages 1 and 2* (2nd edition, 1990). This contains more detailed advice than can be included here.

The points listed below require particular attention.

Teach children never to misuse mains electricity, and warn them of electrical dangers in the home.

Children must never experiment with mains electricity. All investigations of circuits should be done using batteries.

Do not allow children of this age to plug/unplug mains appliances.

Do not cut open batteries since their contents can be corrosive and poisonous.

Do not mix different types of battery in the same battery holder.

Never attempt to recharge batteries which are not intended to be recharged.

2.1 Sources and uses of electricity

AREAS FOR INVESTIGATION

◆ Children's ideas about where electricity comes from.

◆ Warnings about the dangers of mains electricity.

◆ Finding out about electrical appliances which use batteries and mains electricity.

A LOOK AT sources and uses of electricity

KEY IDEAS

◆ Electricity can be produced in power stations and from batteries.

◆ Electricity can be extremely dangerous.

◆ Electricity can be used in different ways to provide lighting and heating, and to make things work.

The mains supply and batteries are both sources of electricity. Mains electricity comes from power stations through overhead and underground cables. To keep producing electricity the power stations need a continuous supply of fuel, such as coal, oil or gas.

Many household items work on mains electricity – for example the television and refrigerator. These appliances are plugged into the mains electricity supply at a wall socket. All appliances, as well as most sockets, have switches so that the supply can be switched on and off. Although these appliances are quite safe if properly used, mains electricity can be very dangerous and it should not be used in any electricity investigations.

Batteries are a safe and convenient source of electricity, and so we use them in toys and portable radios and for electricity experiments.

Some toys and games use solar power to supply their electricity. This is another safe source of electricity. They may also have batteries to keep them going in a dark place.

Finding out children's ideas

■ STARTER ACTIVITIES

Children will have come across household items that use mains electricity, and toys and games which are battery powered.

Find out how much the children are aware of electricity in their lives.

 Can you think of anything which needs electricity to work?
What can you tell me about electricity?
Where do you think electricity comes from?
How is electricity made?
What do you think electricity is like?
Do you think batteries are safe to use?

Children could talk about these questions or write and draw their responses.

Children's ideas

Sources of electricity

Explanations like the following show that children have a wide range of ideas about electricity being produced, which include lightning and Sun.

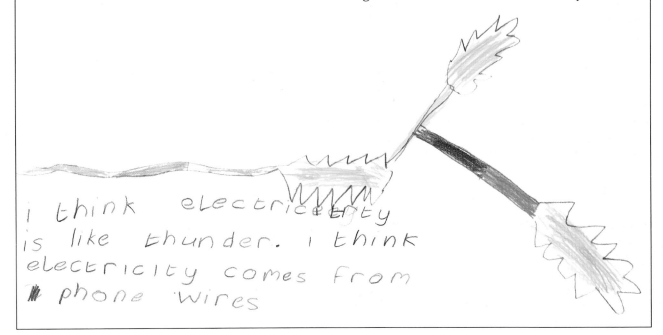

Electricity comes from lightning. It goes underground – it comes up again. When it's another rainy day – it makes more electricity when lightning comes.

It comes from TV.
From the Sun.

There's a man who rubs the stones. Some things come out and make electricity.

i think electricity
is like thunder. i think
electricity comes from
phone wires

Children may confuse electricity with gas.

Electricity is hot ... fire ... comes from big gas things.

Some children suggest that electricity comes from underground and comes by wires.

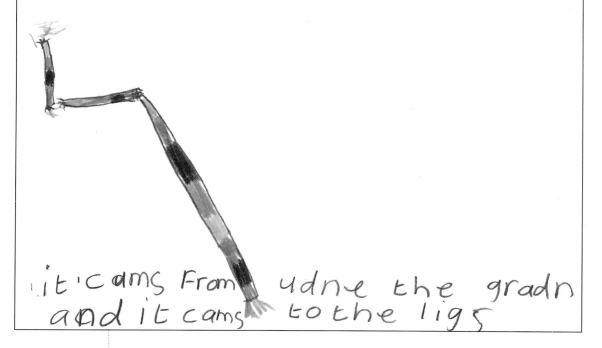

From the ground. Men put electricity in the ground with a big machine – it gives electricity to the ground.

It comes from water. The thing in the middle spins around and makes electricity – I've seen it on the TV.

it cams From udne the gradn and it cams to the ligs

Some children may be aware that electricity comes from power stations, but they are often confused about the details of how it is generated and how it reaches homes, schools and factories.

Electricity from batteries

Many children are familiar with batteries from playing with electrical toys and cassette players, and consider that they provide a safe source or form of electricity – for example:

Batteries are not dangerous to use because you can't see the electricity.

Batteries are safe because all the electricity is inside them.

If you touch it with your hand it does not electrocute you.

Uses of electricity

Children are aware of a wide range of uses for electricity, particularly those in their homes.

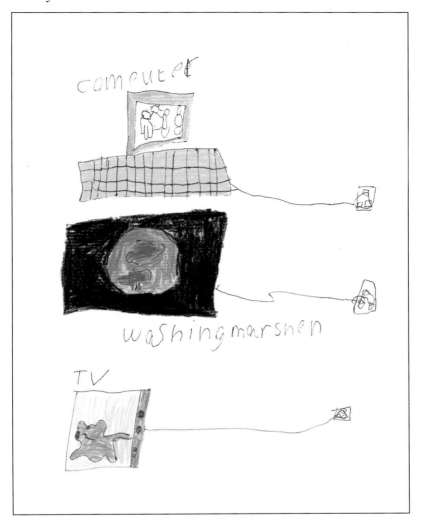

Electricity makes lights shine up.
If you touch electricity you will get an electric shock.

Dangers of electricity

Many children are already aware of some of the dangers of electricity.

If you touch it ... it will electrocute you!

Burns you ... when I was a baby, I went to hospital.

It's dangerous .... it's hot .... your hands will stick to it.

It can be dangerous if you mess around with it and pull out the wires.

If you wash your hands and you do not dry them you might get hurt.

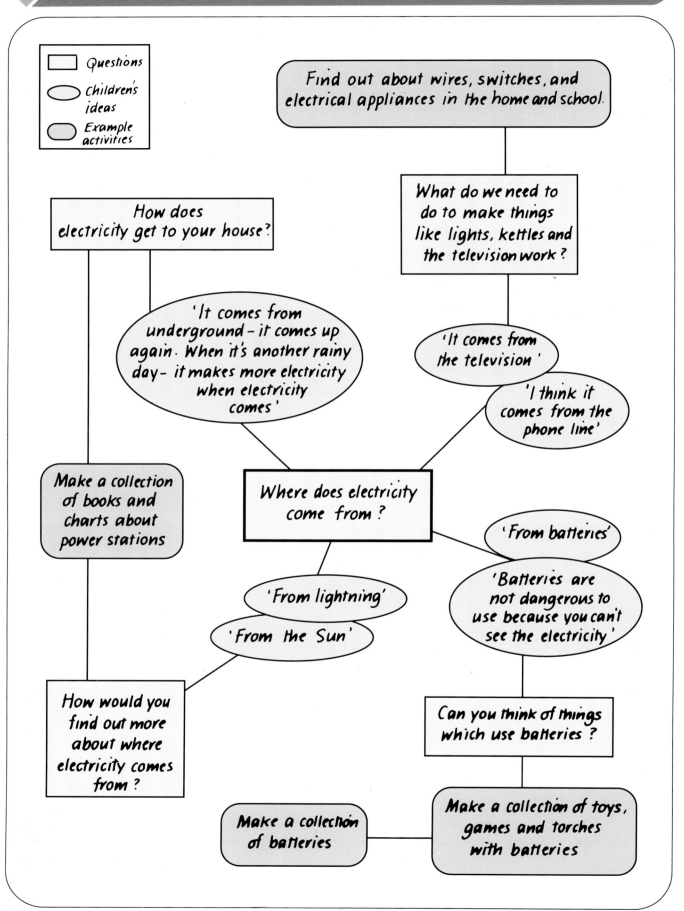

Questions

Children's ideas

Example activities

Find out about wires, switches, and electrical appliances in the home and school.

What do we need to do to make things like lights, kettles and the television work?

How does electricity get to your house?

'It comes from underground – it comes up again. When it's another rainy day – it makes more electricity when electricity comes'

'It comes from the television'

'I think it comes from the phone line'

Make a collection of books and charts about power stations

Where does electricity come from?

'From batteries'

'Batteries are not dangerous to use because you can't see the electricity'

'From lightning'

'From the Sun'

How would you find out more about where electricity comes from?

Can you think of things which use batteries?

Make a collection of batteries

Make a collection of toys, games and torches with batteries

Helping children to develop their ideas

The chart on the previous page shows how you can help children to develop their ideas from starting points which have given rise to different ideas.

At the start of this work it is important to stress to all children that the mains supply can be extremely dangerous.

A first look at electricity and magnets shows some of the hazards associated with electricity and encourages children to think about the ways in which they can use electricity safely.

Batteries are Safe.

Mains electricity can kill you! Never experiment with anything that plugs in.

We may need to help children to distinguish between mains electricity and the safe form of electricity from batteries. Many will have replaced batteries in their toys and games, and will know that it is not possible to get a shock from a small battery. Others may be anxious about using electrical components such as connecting wires because they have been told that 'all wires are dangerous'.

It is important to reassure children that wires attached to batteries are safe to touch; but be sure that they understand that wires attached in any way to the mains can be dangerous.

1 Uses and sources of electricity

Let the children draw pictures of all the things they can think of which use electricity. They could think of these under different headings:

- electricity in the home;
- electricity in school;
- toys which use electricity;
- electricity in the street.

Children could find out which things in school use electricity.

t Set children a good example by switching a socket off before plugging in or out

! Mains electricity can be extremely dangerous

pb

! Under the Electricity at Work regulations, all portable mains appliances should be subjected to a check organized by the employer. Do not be tempted to bring appliances in from home

t We have many electrical appliances in our schools and homes

Q *What kind of things can you find which use electricity? Where are most electrical things found?*

Children could record their findings as a graph or in sets. There would be an opportunity to use a computer to plot a graph.

In the kitchen   In the lounge   In my bedroom

A first look at electricity and magnets gives examples of things in the home and the street which use electricity. It also gives information about the supply of electrical power to the home, paying for electricity, and power stations.

Q *How does the electricity come into the school?*

2 Looking at batteries as sources of electricity

Children could look at and draw various 'dry' batteries – that is, ordinary small ones.

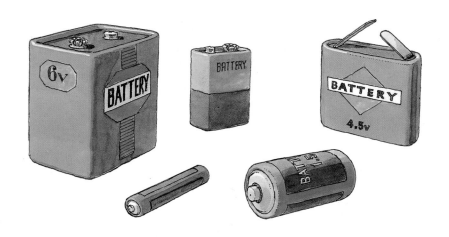

 pb

t Electricity is carried by overhead or underground cables

e

! Children should not cut open batteries, since these contain harmful chemicals. Do not offer rechargeable batteries for examination, since the chemicals in these are particularly poisonous. Do not offer the tiny button batteries – children may swallow them. Discard old batteries, which may leak

t Batteries provide a safe and convenient form of electricity

A first look at electricity and magnets gives examples of everyday items which need batteries and could be used as a starting point.

Q *Are all the batteries the same?*
What are the main differences between them?

The children could predict what might happen if they used different batteries. They could look carefully at the batteries, finding where and how they would attach wires.

A first look at electricity and magnets looks at rechargeable batteries used to drive milk floats. This could be a basis for discussion about this type of battery.

3 Other sources of electricity: solar power

Make a collection of solar powered watches and calculators. The children could find out about the conditions needed to make them work.

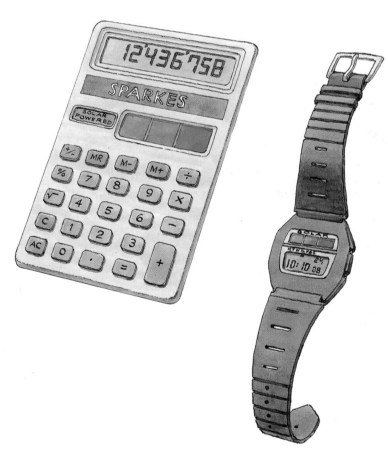

2.2 Making circuits

A LOOK AT simple circuits

Batteries and bulbs have two points of connection. To light a bulb, each battery connection must be joined to a separate bulb connection, forming a complete circuit. Breaking the circuit by disconnecting a wire stops the flow of electricity, and the bulb goes out.

A switch is a very convenient way of turning a light-bulb on or off. When the switch is operated the circuit is completed and the bulb lights up; when the circuit is broken the bulb goes out.

Any material through which electricity passes is called an electrical conductor. Metals are very good conductors of electricity. Materials that conduct almost no electricity are known as insulators; some examples are plastic, wood and paper.

Finding out children's ideas

■ STARTER ACTIVITIES

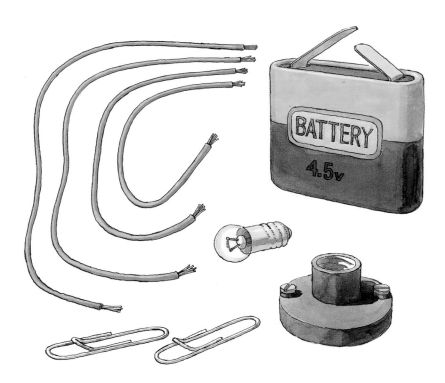

During this work the children should be given the opportunity to make predictions before they try out their ideas. They should test their own ideas rather than being told exactly what to do

Give children an opportunity to look at various kinds of electrical components.

 Can you make the bulbs light up?
Can you draw a picture to show how you would make a bulb light up?

Later, when the children have practical experience of connecting light-bulbs in a circuit, you could find out if they think that all electrical components should be connected in this way. In other words, are the children able to make any generalizations about circuits?

Do children think that a buzzer should be connected in the same way as a light-bulb?

 Can you draw a picture to show how you would connect a buzzer to a battery?

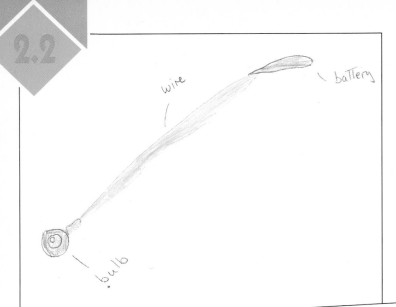

Children's ideas

Children often think that they only need to attach one wire from a battery to a component. This is understandable, since the appearance of an ordinary flex suggests that there is only one wire connecting common household appliances to the mains supply. Children may continue to draw one wire from a battery to a bulb or buzzer, even though this failed to work when they tried it.

Other children find it difficult to observe closely and to identify the connections on a component, especially those on a light-bulb or battery.

With experience of connecting electrical components in circuits, some children are able to give clear descriptions and diagrams of an electrical circuit, as these examples show.

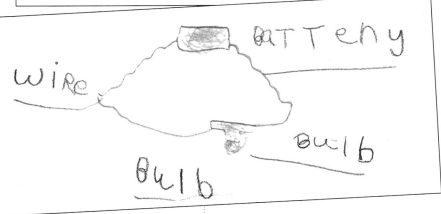

You put two clips at the side and the top. One at the top and one at the bottom, and it goes on.

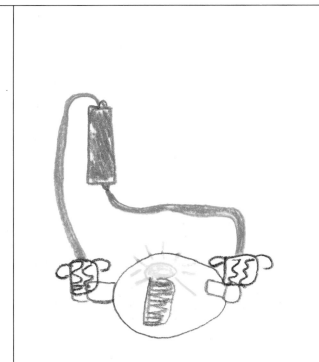

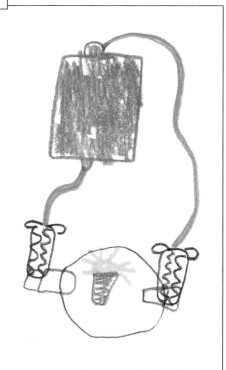

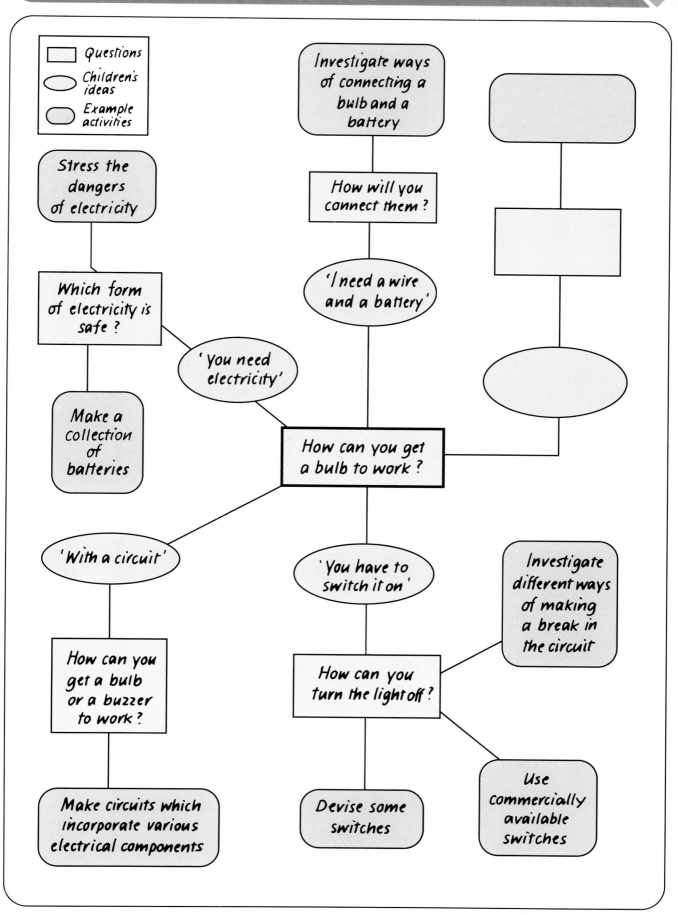

Questions
Children's ideas
Example activities

Stress the dangers of electricity

Which form of electricity is safe?

Make a collection of batteries

'you need electricity'

'With a circuit'

How can you get a bulb or a buzzer to work?

Make circuits which incorporate various electrical components

Investigate ways of connecting a bulb and a battery

How will you connect them?

'I need a wire and a battery'

How can you get a bulb to work?

'You have to switch it on'

How can you turn the light off?

Devise some switches

Investigate different ways of making a break in the circuit

Use commercially available switches

Helping children to develop their ideas

The chart on the previous page shows how you can help children to develop their ideas from starting points which have given rise to different ideas.

e

1   Making circuits

If children try to work out their own explanation of how we can light a bulb before they build a circuit, they are more likely to understand why their circuit works (or doesn't).

Encourage them to examine some electrical components, and to predict what they will need to light a bulb or make a buzzer work.

Q *What do you think you will need to light up a light-bulb?*

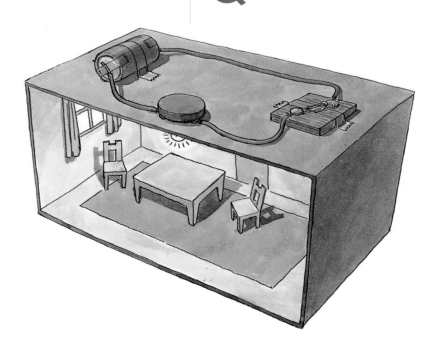

Rather than simply getting the children to devise circuits, you may wish the use of an electrical component to arise as part of a topic; for example, installing a light in a model house or car.

Encourage the children to think about where the electricity will come from, how to get a bulb to work, and how to switch it off.

Once children have connected equipment into a circuit they could make careful drawings showing how the wires connect.

When the children have successfully made their own electric circuits, encourage them to exchange ideas.

Q *What made the bulb light?*
Where did the electricity come from?
How did the electricity get to the bulb?
What are the wires for?
Is it important where you connect the wires?
Can you connect the wires to the battery in more than one way?

To show their ideas, the children could make a careful drawing of their circuit and add their own explanation to it. Alternatively, you could write their explanations for them.

It may not be possible to answer all the children's questions immediately, but they could provide starting points for further exploration.

2   Switches

To save batteries from running down quickly, get the children to disconnect the electrical components from the batteries.

Q *Can you think of as many ways as possible of turning the light out?*

When the children have found several ways of turning their lights out, get them to show these to other children and to share their ideas.

Discuss why undoing one of the connections makes the light go out.

Q *Why do you think the light goes out?*
How can you make the light come back on again?

To help children to develop their ideas about how switches work, give them a range of additional materials.

Q *Can you make a switch using these materials?*

AT 1
Observing
Interpreting results
and findings

t
For electricity to flow, there
must be a circuit

AT 1
Hypothesizing

t
A break in a circuit stops
the flow of electricity

e
t
A switch is a convenient
way of completing or breaking
a circuit

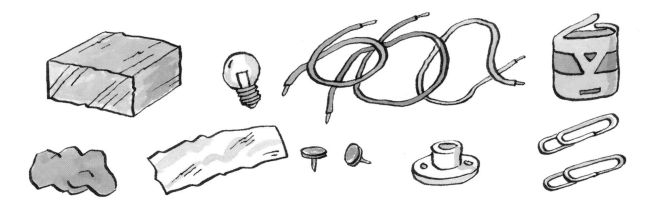

When children have successfully made their own switches, they could draw and write explanations of how switches work. Encourage them to discuss their ideas.

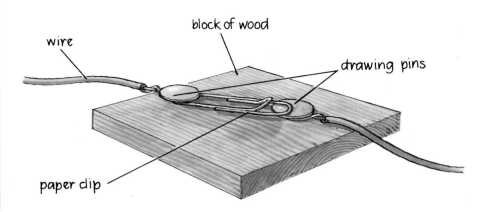

wire

block of wood

drawing pins

paper clip

pb

A first look at electricity and magnets shows some switches which control domestic electrical appliances.

3 Putting lights in models

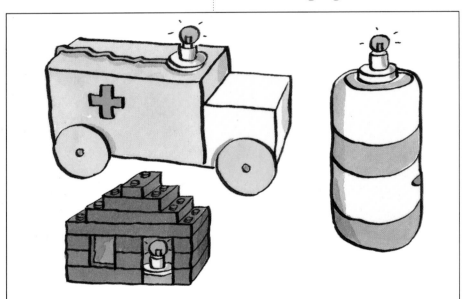

Children could make many different models which incorporate a light and switch.

Children may wish to change the colour of a light in their model. How they tackle this problem will depend on their previous experiences with transparent, translucent and opaque materials. (See the *Light* teachers' guide.)

4   Testing for conductivity

If children use plastic covered wires with plugs or clips attached to the ends, they may think the wires are actually made of plastic. Encourage them to look closely at the wires and to suggest what they think they are made of.

 What do you think wires are made of?
Why do we need to use metal wires?
Do you think electricity will go through other things such as plastic bricks, scissors and so on?
Can you think how you could find out if electricity will go through these?

Let children observe circuits made by different children, and exchange ideas about why some circuits conduct electricity while others do not.

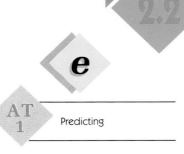

AT
1
Predicting

t   Only some materials conduct electricity

31

2.3 Magnets

◆ Exploring materials to find which are attracted to magnets.

◆ Using magnets in games.

◆ Finding out about the strength of different magnets.

◆ Magnets are mostly made of iron or steel.

◆ Magnets can also attract and repel each other.

◆ * Magnets can produce pushes and pulls (forces) and so attract iron and steel objects.

(*Asterisks indicate ideas which will be developed more fully in later key stages.)

A LOOK AT magnets

Simple magnets are made from iron or steel. Magnets can be different shapes and sizes.

Iron and steel are pulled (attracted) towards a magnet. The pull acts through materials such as paper, plastic and wood. The pull is greatest near the ends of the magnet (the poles). With a bar or horseshoe magnet, it is easy to observe where the poles are.

Materials other than iron or steel are not attracted to magnets. (Actually there are a few other magnetic substances, but these are not normally encountered.)

When we bring magnets near each other we can experience the pulls and pushes acting between them.

A compass needle is a small bar magnet free to turn on a pivot, and the Earth's magnetism causes it to settle in a north–south direction.

Finding out children's ideas

■ STARTER ACTIVITIES

Many children may not have encountered magnets before. Provide them with a whole variety of items which include magnets (of different shapes and sizes) and other objects which are made of different materials including metal.

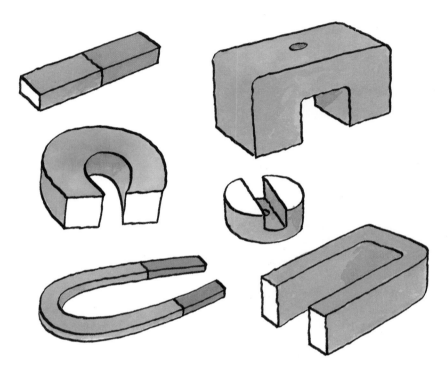

Q *What is a magnet?*
Can you show me which of these are magnets?
How could you find out which of these are magnets?

If the children have not encountered magnets before, you may wish to let them explore magnets in various ways (suggested in the next section) before asking them any further questions.

If the children can recognize a magnet, ask them to explain their ideas about how a magnet works.

Q *How do you think a magnet works?*

Children's ideas

Many children may not have come across a magnet before. Even if they have, school magnets may look quite different from those used in games and toys; for example, magnets used in refrigerator stickers are covered in plastic and children may not know that there is a piece of metal inside.

Some children are aware that magnets attract other objects, but they may not have clear ideas about the kinds of material that are attracted.

> *Magnets stick metals, steel, plastic and other things.*
>
> *A magnet sticks to everything, but it doesn't stick to them because it's too light – it's not strong enough.*
>
> *It sticks to metal, just metal.*

Although some children are aware that magnets can repel each other, they may have difficulty in expressing this idea.

> *It feels a bit hard and it goes like soft.*
>
> *It feels like there is a magic ball between them.*
>
> *Sometimes they push away and sometimes they don't.*

Children may think that magnets have magical properties, or they may try to associate a magnet with other items that 'stick'.

Here are some explanations from young children.

> *It has some sort of glue inside it.*
>
> *It has all these little things inside it which makes it stick.*
>
> *It has got lots of energy and it makes it attract things.*

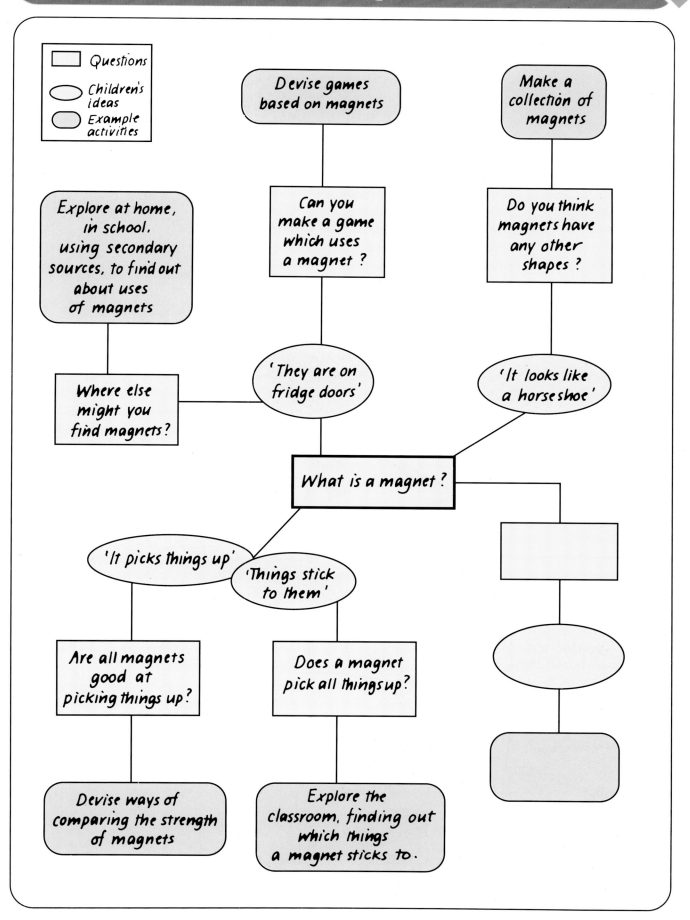

Questions

Children's ideas

Example activities

Devise games based on magnets

Make a collection of magnets

Explore at home, in school, using secondary sources, to find out about uses of magnets

Can you make a game which uses a magnet?

Do you think magnets have any other shapes?

Where else might you find magnets?

'They are on fridge doors'

'It looks like a horseshoe'

What is a magnet?

'It picks things up'

'Things stick to them'

Are all magnets good at picking things up?

Does a magnet pick all things up?

Devise ways of comparing the strength of magnets

Explore the classroom, finding out which things a magnet sticks to.

Helping children to develop their ideas

The chart on the previous page shows how you can help children to develop their ideas from starting points which have given rise to different ideas.

1 Exploration of magnets

Give the children the opportunity to explore for themselves some of the properties of magnets by providing them with a selection of different magnets, magnetic building games, magnetic refrigerator door 'stickers' and similar things.

Q *Which things are attracted to a magnet?*

Give the children a collection of different objects and materials, including some made of metal.

Magnets pull (attract) other iron or steel materials towards them

Q *Which of these things do you think a magnet will pick up?*

AT 1   Predicting

I think a magnet will pick up

I think a magnet will not pick up

The children could do this by sorting the objects into two sets, and recording their predictions of what will happen. They can test their ideas to see if they were right.

Encourage the children to make generalizations about the kind of objects which are attracted to a magnet.

 Q *Can you tell me anything about the things which a magnet will pick up?*
What helps you to decide whether a magnet will pick something up?

Children could write and draw their ideas about how a magnet works. Encourage them to talk about their ideas.

A first look at electricity and magnets looks at the effect of a magnet on objects and materials found in a classroom.

2 Testing the strength of magnets

Get the children to think of how strong the magnets are.

 Q *Which of these magnets do you think will pick up the most paper-clips?*
What makes you think this one will pick up more?
How could you find out?

Get the children to discuss their ideas about how they could carry out their experiment and how they would be able to compare their results.

Children may need help to construct a fair test.

 Q *Will you only dip the magnet into the pile of paper-clips once?*
Will you count how many paper-clips are on just one end of the magnet or both ends?
Should everybody carry out the test using the same kind of paper-clips?

The children could record their findings by drawing the magnet, and showing the number of paper-clips picked up next to it or by making bar graphs. They could use the computer to plot a graph.

AT
1   Interpreting results and findings

pb

AT
1   General

e

t   Magnets differ in strength

 it

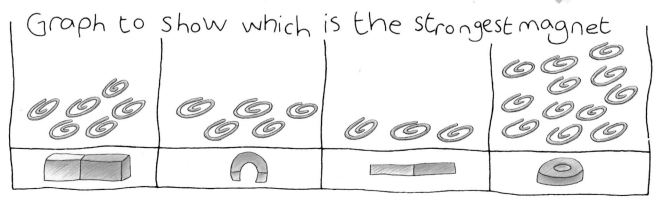

Graph to show which is the strongest magnet

If children are unable to deal with large numbers they could use heavier objects, such as small nails, so that fewer are picked up.

Q *Will magnets work through different materials?*

Children can predict and then test to see if a magnet is capable of working through different materials such as a table, a book, a variety of fabrics, card, paper and so on.

This idea could be extended by asking if a magnet will work through one, two or more sheets of paper.

The children could use this idea to invent some magnetic games.

Children could make magnetic pictures to accompany a story, perhaps one they have made up themselves. Figures can be made for the characters in the story, paper-clips attached at the back, and the figures moved around with magnets behind a cardboard backdrop as the children tell the story.

3 Magnetic poles

Children are likely to discover that magnets stick to each other or push each other apart.

Children could use these observations to design and make their own games such as this 'cops and robbers' game.

 It is inappropriate for children at Key Stage 1 to learn about magnetic poles in a scientific sense

One magnet has a card police officer attached to it, the other has a robber. As long as the children have the same type of pole near each other, the two characters will stay apart. If one magnet swings round, the 'cop' will catch the 'robber'.

Other ideas might include 'cat and mouse', or 'big fish and little fish'.

You may also provide them with games which help them in other curriculum areas.

Children could fish for magnetic words – the idea being that they need to catch a matching pair of words or have enough words to make up a sentence.

They could fish for numbers. For example, children could catch cards on which there are numbers or symbols, and use them for addition and subtraction to amass the highest total.

4 Using magnets in our everyday lives

Children could discuss where they have noticed magnets, or you might make some suggestions of how magnets are used and ask the children to think of what the magnets do in these cases.

Q *How could magnets be useful at a rubbish dump?*
How would a tailor or dressmaker pick up a lot of pins?
How could the school secretary keep the paper-clips together?
Could the magnets work on other doors, apart from refrigerator doors?
Why do they work here?

These could be starting points for children to think about further projects.

◆ They could make a 'recycling plant' for cans as part of a litter project. (Make sure litter is clean. If in doubt they must wear protective gloves or small plastic bags over their hands).

◆ They could design a device for helping elderly or handicapped people pick things up.

◆ They could make door fasteners for a model house.

t Food cans are steel and attracted by a magnet. Some drinks cans are also steel with a non-magnetic aluminium top

CHAPTER 3

Assessment

3.1 Introduction

You will have been assessing your children's ideas and skills by using the activities in this teachers' guide. This on-going, formative assessment is essentially part of teaching since what you find is immediately used in suggesting the next steps to help the children's progress. But this information can also be brought together and summarized for purposes of recording and reporting progress. This summary of performance has to be in terms of National Curriculum level descriptions at the end of the key stages, and some schools keep records in terms of levels at other times.

This chapter helps you summarize the information you have from children's work in terms of level descriptions. Examples of work relating to the theme of this guide are discussed and features which indicate activity at a certain level are pointed out to show what to look for in your pupils' work as evidence of achievement at one level or another. It is necessary, however, to look across the full range of work, and not judge from any single event or piece of work.

There are two sets of examples provided. The first is the assessment of skills in the context of the activities related to the concepts covered in this guide. The second deals with the development of these concepts.

3.2 Assessment of skills (AT1)

Things to look out for when pupils are investigating magnetism and electricity as indicating progress from level 1 to level 3:

Level 1: Making observations of simple properties of magnets and electrical devices such as that they can be controlled by a switch; talking about and drawing them.

Level 2: Making suggestions as well as responding to others' suggestions about how to find things out about a simple circuit or compare materials in terms of magnetic properties. Using equipment, such as batteries, wires, bulbs and bulb holders and magnets, to make observations. Recording what they find and comparing it with what they expected.

Level 3: Saying what they expect to happen when something is changed and suggesting ways of collecting information to test their predictions. Carrying out fair tests, knowing why they are fair, and making measurements. Recording what they find in a variety of ways; noticing any patterns in it.

Children in Year 1 had been playing a mathematics game in which they had to 'fish for numbers' with magnets. They had also used magnetic letters on a steel board to make up words. The teacher encouraged Toby and James to pursue their interest in magnets through an investigation which came about in the following way. The teacher asked them:

What is a magnet?

Both children were able to make suggestions, and appeared to agree on the following:

> *Things stick to magnets.*
> *They are on fridges.*
> *They attract things like iron, brass and gold.*

After showing the children two magnets, the teacher asked:

> *What do you think would happen if we bring these two magnets together?*

Toby and James suggested:

> *They will stick.*

(The teacher had chosen magnets that were different in shape, colour and magnetic strength.)

Toby and James then set about testing the magnets in various ways. Some of the comments they made were as follows.

> *They push away a little bit or stick together like a tube train.*
> *It feels like there is a balloon between them.*
> *They make my hand go round and round.*

As they worked, the children tried investigating how the magnets were attracted to metal objects. The teacher asked:

> *Do you think that the magnets are different in any way?*

James suggested:

> *The red one sticks more. It's more strong.*

In reply, the teacher asked:

> *How can you show that one magnet is stronger than the other?*

Although the children were able to make various suggestions and try out some of their ideas, they were dissatisfied because the methods they used depended on feeling the effects of forces. They reported to the teacher that they were unable to devise a way of answering her question.

In response, the teacher gave them a large pile of paper-clips and asked:

> *What do you think will happen if you try 'fishing' for paper-clips with these magnets?*

James suggested:

> *More will stick all over the red one.*

The teacher gave the children a third magnet and asked:

> *Can you find out which of the magnets is the strongest and which is the weakest?*

(The third magnet was different from the other magnets in shape and magnetic strength.)

The children tested the magnets and showed their results in a picture.

After the children had completed their test, and as they discussed their results with each other, the teacher heard James tell Toby:

Just 'cause a magnet is the biggest it doesn't mean it's the strongest.

Later, both Toby and James were able to tell the teacher about how the magnets compared in magnetic strength, and each of them justified their conclusions by reference to the number of clips attracted to the magnet.

Toby and James made observations of the push and pull between the magnets and were able to describe what they felt, as required for level 1. However, in responding to the teacher's suggestions they showed that they could go beyond this. They did try out their own way of comparing the strength of magnets but realized its difficulties and were quick to seize on the use of the paper-clips. James made a prediction that more would stick to one of the magnets and followed this up with a practical investigation. In comparing the strengths, they made relevant observations and James' drawing shows that they counted the number of paper-clips. This work meets the criteria for level 2 and shows, in the quantification of findings and the way in which they made interpretations, some progress towards level 3. However, there is no evidence here of attempting a fair test, a crucial aspect of achievement at level 3.

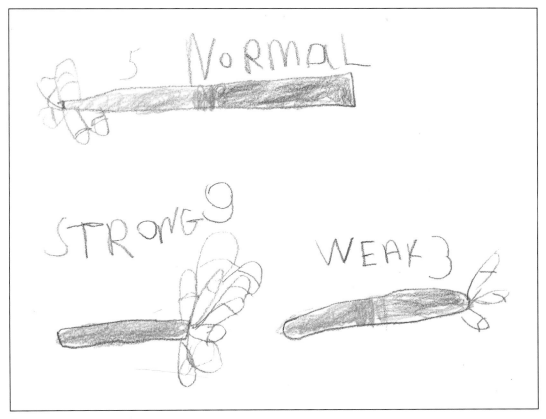

James

3.3 Assessment of children's understanding (Part of AT4)

In terms of work relating to electricity and magnetism, progression from level 1 to level 3 is indicated by:

Level 1: Awareness that many everyday appliances use electricity which can be switched on and off.

Level 2: Constructing a simple electrical circuit to make a bulb light; sorting materials according to whether or not they are magnetic.

Level 3: Knowing that an unbroken circuit is needed to make a bulb light and using this knowledge to suggest why a bulb in a particular circuit may not light up. Knowing that there is attraction and repulsion between magnets and attraction between magnets and magnetic materials.

Sean and Ruth drew their pictures after a discussion with their teacher about household electrical appliances and about some of the dangers associated with electricity in such appliances.

Sean

You can get a shock if you play with it. If you take a plug out with it on you get a shock, if you turn it off you won't get a shock. If you put an oven on hot for something that needs it low the house might set alight.

Ruth

Ruth has shown some electrical appliances and her annotated drawing indicates an awareness of the dangers associated with mains electricity. However, she does not indicate switches or safe use of the appliances. Her work has not yet reached level 1. By contrast Sean's reference to switches and taking a plug out indicate work which is at level 1.

In a Year 2 class the teacher introduced John and Annie to some work on simple circuits. The children already had some experience of batteries from examining torches, electrical toys and games and drawing pictures to show how batteries are connected to these devices. They looked at a collection of electrical components which included connecting wires, crocodile clips, bulbs, bulb holders and a selection of batteries, discussed what the components might be called and suggested how they could be used in electric circuits. After their discussion the teacher asked them to choose some components to light a bulb, and to show, in a picture, how the components might be connected. Annie's first picture is shown at the top of the next page.

After trying out these ideas the children connected the components in various other ways, sometimes attempting to light the bulb without a battery. As the children worked the teacher encouraged them by asking questions.

What is going to light your bulb?
How will you connect the battery to the bulb? What will you use?
How many connections do you think you need on a battery?

Eventually, Annie succeeded in getting her bulb to light, and showed her circuit to John. The children drew pictures of their circuits and told the teacher about them.

You put the clip on to the bulb, and the other clip on, and you connect it to the top of the battery, and put the other on to the battery and it lights up.

Annie suggested trying another type of battery in the circuit, and connected it, as shown at the bottom of page 46.

The teacher asked the children to find ways of switching the bulb on and off. Annie worked quickly, found some ways, and went on to connect an electric motor into a circuit, as shown on page 47. She also described how the motor could be switched on and off.

You take a wire off and it goes off, or a crocodile clip. It won't go because you need two.

John found a number of ways of switching the bulb on and off, and showed them in his picture. He also connected an electric motor into a circuit.

Take the crocodile clips off, get the battery off, or the wire from the crocodile clips.

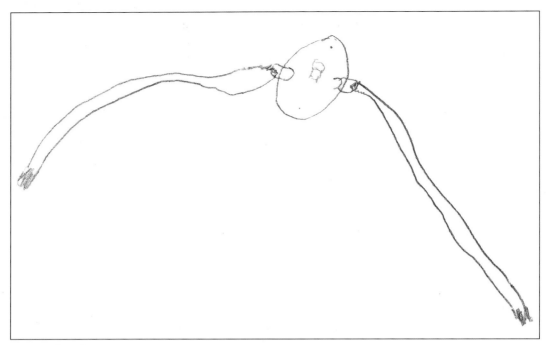

Annie

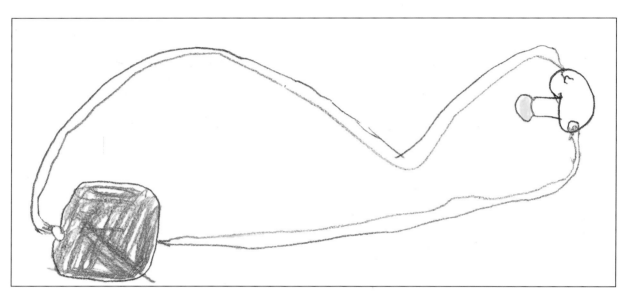

Annie

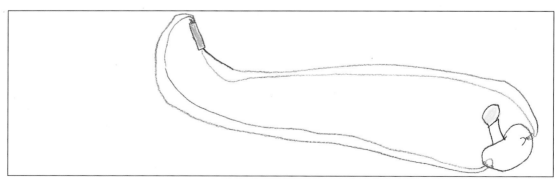

Annie

Annie

John and Annie constructed simple circuits with a bulb and a motor in the circuit and in this respect their work was at Level 2. They also found various ways in which it was possible to switch the bulb or motor on and off by breaking the circuit. This may indicate beginning of awareness that a complete circuit is needed for a device to work and thus progress towards one aspect of level 3.

The teacher could help John and Annie to develop their ideas about a 'complete circuit' in various ways, such as giving them opportunities to:
examine bulbs closely and connect them in circuits, without bulb-holders;
design and construct their own switches;
incorporate a range of electrical devices into their own models;
design and carry out tests on conducting and non-conducting materials;
discuss how the term 'circuit' is used, in a variety of contexts.

John

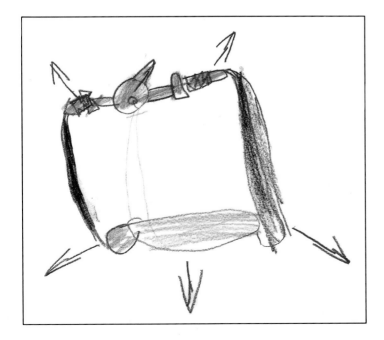

Index

NUFFIELD PRIMARY SCIENCE
Science Processes and Concept Exploration

Directors
Paul Black
Wynne Harlen

Deputy Director
Terry Russell

Project members
Robert Austin
Derek Bell
Adrian Hughes
Ken Longden
John Meadows
Linda McGuigan
Jonathan Osborne
Pamela Wadsworth
Dorothy Watt

First published 1993 by Collins Educational
An imprint of HarperCollins*Publishers*
77-85 Fulham Palace Road
London W6 8JB

Second edition published 1995

Printed and bound in Italy by Rotolito Lombarda, Milan

Design by Carla Turchini, Chi Leung
Illustrations by Mike Dodd, Gay Galsworthy,
Phil Garner, Maureen Hallahan, Mary Lonsdale, Karen
Tushingham, Tony Wells
Cover artwork by Karen Tushingham

Photograph acknowledgements
Page 16: John Birdsall
Page 24: John Birdsall
Page 32: John Birdsall

Commissioned photography by Oliver Hatch

The Trust and the Publishers would like to thank the
governors, staff and pupils of Hillbrook Primary School,
Tooting, for their kind co-operation with many of the
photographs in this book.

Safety adviser
Peter Borrows

Other contributors
Marcella Armstrong
Anne de Normanville